Math Is Everywhere

Story by Brian and Jillian Cutting

Countdown Math

We have lift-off!

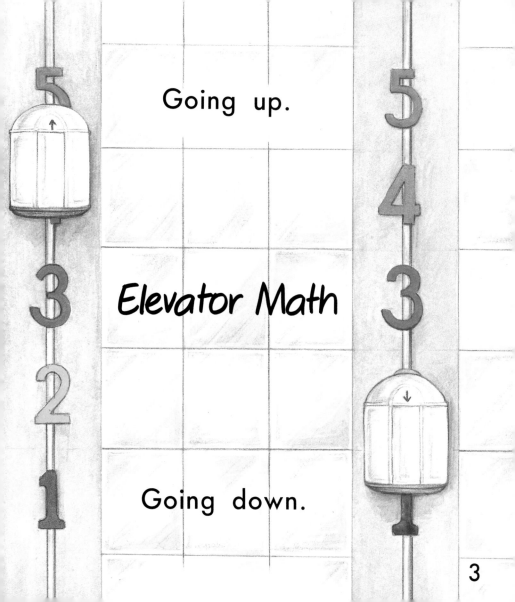

Going up.

Elevator Math

Going down.

Math in the Shop

This dress is too big.

This dress is too small.

This dress is too long.

This dress is just right.

"We'll take this one," says Mom.

Math and the Mouse

The mouse crept **out** of his hole.

He went **across** the floor
and **under** the table.

9

He climbed **up** the leg
and **onto** the table.
Oh! Lovely food!
Oh! Lovely cheese!

11

The mouse went **across** the table.
He sniffed at the cheese.

Bang

Down the leg, **across** the floor,
through the hole, **into** his home.

15

"I hate traps," said the mouse,
"but I love cheese."